EZRA L. PITT
VENTNOR - VIEWS
1, VENTNOR GARDENS
BARKING
ESSEX, IG11 9JY
TEL: 0181 - 594 0173

HOW TO Identify

Addictive

Behaviour

The Promis handbook on cross addictions.

Dr. Robert Lefever

Promis Publishing Limited
1 St. Quintin Avenue
London W10 6NX

© Dr Robert Lefever 1988

First published 1988

ISBN 1 871013 03 8

Designed by Glenn Travis Associates, London

Printed in Great Britain by Biddles Limited, Guildford

To Beauchamp Colclough and Josephine Timmins
and to my wife Meg
with fond memories and anticipations
of the time we spend together
working to learn more about addictive disease
and the happiness to be found in recovery.

Acknowledgements

To Beauchamp Colclough
and the staff and patients of
The PROMIS Recovery Centre
who helped me formulate these ideas.

To my wife's secretary, Susan Kranat
for typing the manuscript

Contents

Introduction

Addiction comes with the person, not with the substance or behaviour. It tends to run in families and may be genetically inherited. This does not mean that if either of your parents have addictive disease then you yourself will necessarily get it in some form or other or that you will necessarily hand it on to your children. But it does mean that there is a chance of this. It is therefore as well to be aware of it.

Addiction is a term that instills fear – and rightly so. Addiction is an inner compulsion, an alien parasite, driving the sufferer to do things that are against his or her own better nature and that are utterly destructive in their consequences.

Addiction is not merely a preference or fondness in the way that one might prefer wine to orange juice or be fond of antique furniture or of one's children or of a game of chess or cricket. Addiction is a compulsion to return to doing something that the sufferer may not even like (and may actively loathe) and despite intellectual knowledge of its damaging consequences.

Further, a sufferer from addiction is "in denial" as part of the basic psycho-pathology of the disease: addiction is a disease that tells the sufferer that he or she does not have it.

The addictive substance or behaviour is used because of its mood-altering properties. In this it works: it *does* alter the mood. Therefore it is treated as a trusted friend. The connection with all the various consequences is simply denied. Sure, these things happen – but that is seen as the fault or responsibility of other people and not the fault or responsibility of the sufferer or associated with his or her specific substances or behaviours of addiction.

But there is hope. Since the birth of Alchoholics Anonymous, more than half a century ago, the understanding of and treatment for addictive disease has advanced miraculously. Addiction can be seen nowadays not as the sad plight of a few pathetic individuals but as an exceedingly common condition affecting large numbers of people in many different ways, although always with similar effects on behaviour and with similar destructive consequences.

The hope comes from the awareness that as more people become conscious of addictive disease so more people will understand it and accept it.

As more people gradually recover from addictive disease, one day at a time, so their lives, and the lives of those around them, become immeasurably richer.

The curse, the threat to recovery, is the "cunning, baffling and powerful" nature of addictive disease itself, as first so aptly described in the "Big Book" of Alchoholics Anonymous. (The "Big Book" is itself termed "Alcoholics Anonymous").

The specific threat to recovery to which this PROMIS Handbook refers is cross-addiction; that no sooner does the sufferer get into recovery from one aspect of addictive disease than it may appear again in another aspect of life.

Thus, the alcoholic in recovery may take to sugar and white flour and develop an eating disorder or, alternatively, take to nicotine in an addictive manner, with all the physical, mental, emotional and spiritual consequences that that implies. Similarly, someone in recovery from drug addiction may go wild on gambling or become power crazy and, in the subsequent turmoil, be at serious risk of relapse back to his or her primary addiction to drugs.

One of the aims of this PROMIS Handbook is for people who are already in recovery from addictive disease to be able to assess their risks of cross-addiction.

The tragedy of relapse (two thirds of the people going to meetings of Anonymous Fellowships, and even one third of all people first going through residential treatment centres, subsequently revert to their primary addiction) may possibly be averted if they become informed in advance of where their addictive disease is lurking, waiting to catch them and bring them down.

Recovery from addictive disease is essentially a spiritual process; a healing of the disturbed senses of hope, trust, love, faith, joy and other spiritual aspects of life. When these are restored through the 12 Step Programme of the Anonymous Fellowships, many or even all of the damaged consequences in physical, mental, emotional, social, financial, marital and other aspects of life gradually resolve. However, spiritual recovery is not possible in each addiction unless the initial substance or behaviour of addiction is put down.

Whilst the only requirement for membership of Alcoholics Anonymous is a desire to stop drinking, nothing of much value will be retained from a meeting of Alcoholics Anonymous if the sufferer was drunk at the time. The first need is to stop using the primary substance or behaviour of addiction. Once that is done, enormous strides are possible with spiritual recovery.

If this is not done, then little or no lasting spiritual and subsequent behavioural recovery will be possible, even though the 12 Steps and other aspects of the recovery programme may be readily recited.

One of the ways in which recovery may be safeguarded is to reduce the unpredictability of risk factors leading to relapse. If a recovering person knows, in addiction to his or her primary addiction, that he or she also has a tendency towards other manifestations of addictive disease, then that is where to look for potential trouble.

In this PROMIS Handbook on cross-addiction are fourteen sets of questionnaires designed to seek out specific areas of primary addiction, and also two questionnaires designed to seek out the "Family Disease" of addiction to self-denial and caretaking. From these questionnaires it is possible to see a picture of the intensity and distribution of the addictive disease in any individual sufferer. Subsequently, it is possible to derive treatment plans and insurance strategies against relapse. After all, if recovery is worth having at all it is worth having well.

One further use of this PROMIS Handbook is to gain an insight into how addictive disease may occur in different forms in various members of the same family. For example, a young sufferer from drug addiction may be seen as the family "problem" until his or her father and mother go through the various questionnaires and perhaps reveal addictions of their own.

My hope is that, in time, addictive disease will be seen and accepted for what it is: an exceedingly common and utterly destructive process that is beyond the self-control of the sufferer but from which, through the Anonymous Fellowships (and sometimes additionally through 12 step treatment centres based upon the principles of the Anonymous Fellowships) recovery is possible.

CHAPTER One

The PROMIS Addiction Questionnaires

Disease causes disturbance in function. Addictive disease causes the sufferer to return at some time to the substance, process or relationship of addiction despite disturbance of function and despite previous negative consequences.

Addiction is in the person, not just in the drug or substance or behaviour

The PROMIS Addiction Questionnaires illustrate the commonality between all forms of addictive disease. A series of similar questions, based upon the same general behavioural characteristics of all addictions, reveals addictive disease in various forms. The sufferer remains the same as in any other form of addiction; only the specific substance or behaviour of choice will vary.

(i) Alcohol

1. Do you feel a physical sense of increased tension or excitement when you enter a public house or look at a wine list or at advertisements for your favourite drink?

2. Do you get irritable and impatient if there is more than ten minutes conversation at a meal or social function before your host offers you a drink?

3. Would it be more painful for you to give up alcohol than to give up a close friendship?

4. Do you not infrequently find that having one drink tends not to satisfy you but to make you want more?

5. Do you tend to gulp down the first drink fairly fast?

1

6. Do you almost prefer to drink alone rather than in company?

7. Have you often had a drink last thing at night to help you to get to sleep or had a drink when you wake-up in the middle of the night?

8. Do you *particularly* enjoy a drink or cocktail that has a real "kick" to it?

9. Do you tend to think of alcoholic drinks not so much as satisfiers of thirst but as rewards that you deserve because of stress you endure?

10. Have you ever drunk the mixed dregs of other peoples' drinks after a party or something else generally considered undrinkable?

11. Have you ever kissed a glass or bottle of drink and told it you loved it?

12. At the time that you anticipated having a drink would you have a drink even though the only drink available was a variety that you do not normally like?

13. Do you like to drink a little and often throughout the day?

14. Do you tend to use alcohol as both a comfort and strength?

15. When you have *definitely* drunk too much do you tend to feel defiant as well as disappointed in yourself?

16. Do you tend to time your drinking as a form of strategy so that others are not really aware of how much you are drinking?

17. Would you have a drink before you go out to a function that might be tea-total?

18. Have you ever regularly stolen from other people or helped yourself to their drink even though you had enough money to buy your own?

19. Would you find it strange to leave a half a glassful of your drink?

20. Do you find that feeling light-headed is often irrelevant in deciding when to stop drinking?

21. Do you have an absolute rule not to drink before a certain time of day *or* have you ever given up alcohol for a week or month or more in order to prove to yourself that you can do without it?

22. Are you aware from your own experience that you commonly drink significantly more than you intended?

23. Are you consciously determined *and* generally proud of your ability to control your drinking?

24. Even when you can perfectly well afford to pay for your own drink, do you nonetheless take the opportunities to drink when someone else is paying or when you can charge it to an expense account?

25. Have you had two or more drunk driving charges or lost two or more jobs or positions of any kind because of your drinking?

26. Has anyone else ever expressed repeated serious concern about your drinking?

27. Have you ever had a complete blank of ten minutes or more in your memory when you try to recall what you were doing when you were drinking on the previous day or night?

28. In your prime did you (or do you now) have a good head for alcohol so that others appear to get drunk more readily than you?

29. Do you find that all of these questions are perfectly straight-forward and none of them a bit strange?

30. Do you feel that you would instinctively understand someone who answered yes to *all* of these questions?

(ii) Nicotine

Drugs of choice – tobacco, cigarettes, cigars, snuff, tobacco bags, nicorette chewing gum.

In this questionnaire please substitute your own nicotine drug of choice for "tobacco" in each question.

1. Do you feel a physical sense of increased tension or excitement when you buy tobacco or look at advertisements?

2. Do you get irritable and impatient if someone offers you tobacco and then chatters on for a few minutes before producing it?

3. Would it be more painful for you to give up tobacco than to give up a close friendship?

4. Do you not infrequently find that having your first use of tobacco in any day tends not to satisfy you but to make you want more?

5. Do you tend to get through the first tobacco fairly fast?

6. Do you almost prefer to use your tobacco alone rather than in company?

7. Do you often take tobacco to calm you nerves?

8. Do you particularly enjoy a really strong brand?

9. Do you tend to think of tobacco not so much as an occasional social activity but primarily as a reward for stresses you endure?

10. Have you ever in adulthood relit the stubbed-out end of a cigarette or a cigarette discarded by a stranger?

11. Have you ever felt a particularly intimate relationship with tobacco so that in a strange way that you are a "real" person only when you are using it?

12. If you had run out of your own favourite brand, would you accept the offer of an alternative that you do not normally like?

13. Do you prefer to use tobacco throughout the day rather than only at specific times?

14. Do you tend to use tobacco as both a comfort and strength even when you do not feel that you particularly want any?

15. When you have definitely used too much tobacco do you tend to feel defiant as well as disappointed in yourself?

16. When you are in company do you tend to disguise just how much tobacco you tend to use?

17. Would you tend to use some tobacco immediately before a social function during which you would not be able to use it?

18. Have you ever regularly stolen or helped yourself to other people's tobacco even though you had enough money to buy your own?

19. Do you find it difficult to leave the last remaining tobacco in a packet?

20. Do you find that feeling a sense of physical wretchedness or even disgust irrelevant in deciding when to stop using tobacco?

21. Have you ever tried to prove to yourself that you are not addicted to tobacco by giving up for a week, a month or more?

22. Are you aware from your own experience that you commonly use significantly more tobacco than you intended?

23. Are you afraid that you will put on excessive amounts of weight or become particularly irritable or depressed if you give up using tobacco altogether?

24. Even when you can perfectly well afford to buy your own tobacco, do you nonetheless take the opportunities to use someone else's?

25. Have you ever continued to use tobacco even when you have bad influenza or even a more serious respiratory problem?

26. Has anyone else ever expressed repeated serious concern over your tobacco consumption?

27. Do you tend to accept an offer of more tobacco substance even when you have just had some and do not particularly feel like having any more?

28. Do you find that your tobacco consumption goes either up or down when you are off alcohol or drugs or when you are on a diet?

29. Do you find that all of these questions are perfectly straightforward and none of them a bit strange?

30. Do you feel that you would instinctively understand someone who answered yes to *all* of these questions?

(iii) Recreational Drugs

Drugs of choice – heroin, cocaine, LSD, magic mushrooms, "Designer" drugs, amphetamines and other stimulants, cannabis, solvents.

1. Do you feel a sense of increased tension and excitement when you know that you have the opportunity to get some drugs?

2. Do you get irritable and impatient if your dealer keeps you waiting for ten minutes for no obvious good reason?

3. Would it be more painful to give up drugs than to give up a close friendship?

4. Do you not infrequently find that you use all the drugs in your possession even though you had intended to spread them out over several occasions?

5. Over the years have you tried several different drugs so that you now take the regular use of cannabis for granted as normal?

6. Do you almost prefer to use drugs on your own rather than with friends?

7. Do you often take a drug last thing at night to help you get to sleep or use a drug if you wake up in the middle of the night?

8. Do you particularly enjoy a really strong effect?

9. Do you tend to think of drugs not so much as occasional pleasures but more as rewards that you deserve because of stress you endure?

10. Have you ever used drugs from a supply contaminated with dirt, obtained drugs from dirty surroundings or have you ever shared a needle with anyone else?

11. Have you ever swapped sex for drugs or for money to buy drugs?

12. If you could not get your drug of choice would you tend to take something else even though you might not know its purity or its anticipated effect on you?

13. Do you tend to make sure that you have drugs or the money for drugs before concentrating on other things?

14. Do you tend to use drugs as both a comfort and strength?

15. When you have *definitely* used more drugs than you intended, do you tend to feel defiant as well as disappointed in yourself?

16. Do you tend to be secretive in your over all use of drugs so that others are not really aware of how much you are using?

17. Would you use drugs before going out for an evening if you were concerned that you might later feel like using them but not have the opportunity to do so?

18. Have you ever regularly stolen things from other people or helped yourself to other people's drugs even when you have enough money to buy your own?

19. Would you find it strange to stub out half a joint?

20. Do you tend to find that getting high tends to relax you so that you go on to take more drugs if they are available?

21. Have you ever tried to prove to yourself that you are not addicted by giving up for a week or month or more?

22. Are you aware from your own experience that if you do have a drink – or a joint or another drug – that you then tend to want more of them or of your own particular drug of choice?

23. Are you consciously determined – and generally proud of your ability – to control your drug use?

24. Do you tend to use more drugs if you have got more, even if you are not concerned by the cost?

25. Have you had two or more drugs related charges by the police or punishments from other authorities?

26. Has anyone else ever expressed repeated serious concern about any aspect of your drug use?

27. Do you tend to be able to hold your drugs well and does it tend to take more or stronger drugs for you to get high than it used to?

28. Do you find that your alcohol or food consumption goes up when you are off drugs?

29. Do you find that all of these questions are perfectly straightforward and none of them disgusting, alarming or strange?

30. Do you feel that you would instinctively understand someone who answered yes to *all* of these questions?

(iv) **Caffeine**

Drugs of choice – Pro Plus, chocolate, cocoa, tea and coffee, lemonade, cola etc.

In this questionnaire please substitute your own caffeine drug of choice for "caffeine" in each question.

1. Do you have a sense of increased tension or excitement when you buy caffeine substances or when you look at advertisements for them?

2. Do you get irritable and impatient if someone has offered you caffeine and then chatters on for ten minutes before serving it?

3. Would it be more painful for you to give up caffeine than to give up a close friendship?

4. Do you not infrequently find that having your first caffeine in any day tends not to satisfy you but to make you want more?

5. Do you tend to gulp down the first cup, bar or packet fairly fast?

6. Do you almost prefer to take caffeine on your own rather than in company?

7. Do you often take caffeine to keep you awake?

8. Do you particularly enjoy strong tea or coffee or rich chocolate or do you frequently take ProPlus or similar caffeine substances?

9. Do you tend to think of caffeine not so much as a satisfier of thirst or hunger but as a reward that you deserve because of stresses you endure?

10. Would you eat chocolate that has melted and then reset so that you have to pick bits of silver paper out of it or would you stew up a teabag that has already been used and thrown into the bin if you discovered you had no more?

11. Have you ever felt that you have an intimate relationship with caffeine so that in a strange way you feel that you are a "real" person only when you are using it.

12. At the time that you would normally take your favourite form of caffeine, would you take one of the alternatives even though you do not normally reckon to like that one?

13. Do you like to keep yourself "topped-up" with caffeine throughout the day?

14. Do you tend to use caffeine as both a comfort and strength?

15. When you have *definitely* eaten, drunk or used too much do you tend to feel defiant as well as disappointed in yourself?

16. Do you tend to time your intake of caffeine so that others are not really aware of your total intake?

17. Do you sometimes rush through a meal or drop it altogether so that you can have some caffeine?

18. Have you ever regularly stolen or helped yourself to other people's caffeine even though you had enough money to buy your own?

19. Do you find it difficult to leave half a bar, cup or pack?

20. Do you find that feeling wide awake is often irrelevant in deciding when to stop using caffeine?

21. Have you ever tried to cut out caffeine altogether for a week, a month or more just to prove that you can do without it?

22. Are you aware from your own experience that you commonly use significantly more caffeine than you intended?

23. Are you consciously determined – and generally proud of your ability – to control your intake of caffeine?

24. Are your frequently capable of eating a half pound bar of chocolate at a sitting or of having twenty cups of tea or coffee or twenty tablets of ProPlus in a day?

25. Have you, on two or more occasions, been so light headed from caffeine that you have made significant mistakes and had damaging consequences?

26. Has anyone else ever expressed repeated serious concern about your intake of caffeine?

27. Do you tend nowadays to need more or stronger intake of caffeine than you previously used in order to get the same effect?

28. Do you find that your intake of another form of caffeine tends to increase when you are off your own favourite and do you find that your food intake goes up significantly when you are off caffeine altogether?

29. Do you find that all of these questions are perfectly straightforward and none of them a bit strange?

30. Would you instinctively understand someone who answered yes to *all* of these questions?

(v) Gambling and Risk Taking

1. Do you feel an overwhelming sense of tension and excitement when you know you are about to gamble or take a significant risk?

2. Do you get irritable and impatient if there is a complete break of ten minutes in a gambling session?

3. Would it be more painful for you to give up gambling or risk-taking than to give up a close friendship?

4. Do you find that your first episode of gambling or risk-taking in any day tends to "trigger" your craving for more?

5. Do you tend to gamble more recklessly than other people and do you often take a risk without really weighing up your chances?

6. Do you almost prefer to gamble on your own rather than in company?

7. Have you often gambled in order to settle your nerves?

8. Do you particularly enjoy gambling or taking risks for high stakes?

9. Do you tend to think of gambling not so much as a pleasant pastime but as a reward that you deserve because of stress that you endure.

10. Have you ever taken bets on something that other people might find shocking or disgusting?

11. Have you ever felt in a strange way that you only become a "real" person when you are gambling or taking risks?

12. If your favourite form of gambling or risk-taking was unavailable at a particular time would you gamble or take risks on something else even if it was at something that you do not normally like?

13. Do you prefer to gamble or take risks in one way or another throughout the day rather than only at particular times?

14. Do you tend to use gambling or risk-taking as a form of comfort and strength even when you do not feel that you particularly want to gamble or take further risks?

15. When you have definitely gambled too much or taken too great a risk do you tend to feel defiant as well as disappointed in yourself?

16. When you are gambling or risk-taking in company do you tend to disguise precisely how much you have at stake over all?

17. Would you gamble or take a risk on the first thing available if the opportunity you anticipated was not yet ready?

18. Have you ever regularly gambled with people whom you knew you could beat so that there was no real pride in achievement?

19. Do you find it difficult to stop gambling before the final end of a session?

20. Do you find that the amount that you have won or lost is often irrelevant in deciding when to stop gambling or taking risks?

21. Have you ever tried to prove to yourself that you are not addicted to gambling or risk-taking by giving up for a week, a month or more?

22. Are you aware from your own experience that you commonly gamble for much longer than you intended?

23. Are you afraid that you will become particularly irritable or depressed if you give up gambling and risk-taking altogether?

24. Have you frequently gambled with people whom you knew could not afford to lose?

25. Have you ever stolen or embezzled to cover gambling or risk-taking losses?

26. Has anyone else expressed repeated serious concern over your gambling or risk-taking?

27. Do you tend to accept opportunities for further gambling or risk-taking despite having just completed a session or project?

28. Do you find that your gambling and risk-taking is increased when you cut down on alcohol or nicotine?

29. Do you find that all of these questions are perfectly straight-forward and none of them a bit strange?

30. Do you feel you would instinctively understand someone who answered yes to *all* of these questions?

(vi) Work

"Behaviour of choice": professional work, hobbies, cults, particular interests.

In this questionnaire please substitute your own behaviour of choice in place of "work" in each question.

1. Do you feel an almost overwhelming sense of excitement when you take on a new project?

2. Do you get irritable and impatient when you find yourself stuck in a situation where there is not enough to do so that you look forward to going back to work?

3. Would it be more painful for you to give up work than to give up a close friendship?

4. Do you not infrequently have so many separate projects going at once that it is difficult if not impossible to keep track of them?

5. Do you tend to work faster and for longer hours than other people of your own ability so that they find it difficult to keep up with you?

6. Do you almost prefer to work alone rather than with others?

7. Have you often taken work to bed with you or away at the weekends or on holiday?

8. Do you particularly enjoy the challenge of working to a deadline and do you tend to work better against the clock?

9. Do you tend to think of work not so much as a means to an end but as a reward and personal happiness that you deserve because of stress that you endure?

10. Have you ever taken on a piece of work that you actively disliked, not so much as an act of necessity or discipline but more simply to keep yourself occupied?

11. Have you ever felt in a strange way that you only become a "real" person when you are working?

12. Do you feel most comfortable when your "in-tray" is so full that you do not really know what is in it?

13. Do you prefer to work straight through the day and evening rather than break it up with periods of relaxation?

14. Do you tend to use work as both a comfort and strength even when there is no particular need for it to be done?

15. When you have definitely overworked and got yourself irritable and overtired do you tend to feel defiant as well as slightly sheepish?

16. When you are working with others do you tend to disguise the full amount of time and effort that you put in to your work?

17. Do you tend to keep reserve projects up your sleeve just in case you find some time – even a few minutes – to spare?

18. Have you ever regularly covered other people's work and responsibilities even when there was no need for you to do so?

19. Do you find it difficult to leave a piece of work unfinished?

20. Do you find that finishing a specific project is often irrelevant in deciding when to stop working?

21. Have you ever tried to stop work altogether – even on holiday for a week or two – just in order to prove that you are not addicted to work?

22. Are you aware from your own experience that once you start work in any day it is difficult to get "out of the swing of it" and relax other than by changing projects?

23. Are you afraid that life would become exceedingly boring and tiresome if you were to retire or stop work for some reason?

24. Do you tend to change your work once you have mastered its daily demands?

25. Have you ever worked on three or more significant projects in entirely different aspects of life at the same time?

26. Has anyone else expressed repeated serious concern over your working habits?

27. Would you take on a new project despite already having a timetable that is impossibly full so that one project or another is almost bound to suffer?

28. Would you tend to tidy up the mess that someone else had got into at work, even if you had not been asked to do so?

29. Do you find that all of these questions are perfectly straight-forward and none of them a bit strange?

30. Do you feel that you would instinctively understand someone who answered yes to *all* of these questions?

(vii) Relationships

"Behaviours of choice": Any repetitive, compulsive activity – either dominant or submissive, potentially damaging to others or poten-tially damaging to yourself – that leaves other people in the situa-tion whereby, out of concern for your actions, they are led to focus much of their attention upon your demands or needs. Thus, addictive relationships with other people may be used as a form of "drug" that is either dominant (stimulant) or submissive (tranquillising) in its effect.

(a) Dominant (stimulant) Relationships

1. Do you feel an almost overwhelming sense of excitement when about to be in a position of power over someone else?

2. Do you get irritable and impatient when people talk about their rights as individuals?

3. Would it be more painful for you to give up your position(s) of power and influence than to give up a close friendship?

4. Do you not infrequently have so much concern over others trying to take away your power or influence that you are repeatedly concerned by "rumours" or "plots" and feel that there are very few people you can trust?

5. Do you tend to look for or take on positions of power and influence so that you rise to a position of emotional or practical power over others as rapidly as possible?

6. Do you so much prefer to be in a position of power or influence that you find it exceedingly difficult to work as a genuinely equal member of a team?

7. Do you find it difficult to sleep or to relax when you feel that others have power over you?

8. Do you particularly enjoy knowing that much of other people's lives depends on your actions or decisions?

9. Do you tend to think of power not so much as the partner of responsibility but as a reward that you deserve because of stress that you endure?

10. Have you ever taken a position of power that other people might find emotionally disturbing or morally disgusting?

11. Have you ever felt in a strange way that you only become a "real" person when you are in a position of power over someone else?

12. Have you ever taken a position of power and influence even though you did not like the activity involved?

13. Do you prefer to have power and influence in all your relationships, rather than risk being vulnerable?

14. Do you tend to use a position of power or influence as a comfort and strength regardless of whether there are particular deficiencies needing your attention in other aspects of your life?

15. When you have definitely gone too far and taken advantage of your position(s) of power and influence, do you tend to feel defiant as well as slightly sheepish?

16. When you are with others do you tend to disguise just how much power and influence you truly have and always prefer to keep them guessing?

17. Do you tend to disregard other personal aspects of life when you feel that your position of power or influence is under threat?

18. Have you regularly undermined other people's positions of power or influence even though they may have significantly less than your own?

13

19. Do you find it difficult not to take up a position of power or influence when it is available, even when you do not really need it and can see no particular use for it?

20. Do you find that having all the power and influence that you need for your own personal and professional life is irrelevant in deciding when to stop seeking more?

21. Have you ever resigned a position of power or influence just to prove to yourself that power and influence are not in themselves important to you?

22. Are you aware from your own experience that, once you start work in any relationship or project, you are uncomfortable until yours is the dominant power or influence?

23. Are you afraid that your life will fall apart and that people will take advantage of you if you give up the power and influence you currently hold?

24. Do you tend to look for new opportunities for power and influence once you have mastered any specific position?

25. Have you ever had three or more positions of power or influence in entirely distinct spheres of life at the same time?

26. Has anyone else expressed repeated serious concern over your use of power or influence?

27. Would you take on a new position of power or influence even though you find it difficult to manage those you already have?

28. Would you take over someone else's position of power and influence if the opportunity arose to do so even if you had not been asked to do so by that person or by anyone else?

29. Do you find that all of these questions are perfectly straightforward and none of them disturbing or strange?

30. Do you feel that you would instinctively understand someone who answered yes to *all* of these questions?

(b) Submissive (Tranquillising) Relationships

1. Do you feel an almost overwhelming sense of excitement when you find a new person to look after your needs or a new way in which an existing close person can look after them better?

2. Do you tend to get irritable and impatient when people look after themselves rather than you?

3. Would you tend to think that a close friendship is when someone *really* looks after you?

4. Do you tend to take actions that have progressively more damaging effects on yourself or on your possessions?

5. Have you attempted suicide more than once?

6. Do you tend to be upset if someone close to you takes care of someone else?

7. Do you feel most in control of your feelings when other people are performing services of one kind or another for you?

8. Do you not infrequently find that you get totally swept off your feet in any new close relationship?

9. Do you tend to search for someone to *really* understand you and the stresses you endure?

10. Have you repeatedly done things to yourself that other people would tend to find emotionally disturbing or disgusting?

11. Have you ever felt in a strange way that you only become a "real" person when you are being totally looked after by someone else?

12. Have you ever allowed yourself to be in a continuing close relationship with someone you do not really like?

13. Do you try to avoid any risk of being hurt by other people?

14. Do you tend to use a close relationship as a comfort and strength even though this relationship may diminish the quality and variety of your life?

15. When you have definitely taken the concern of someone else for granted do you tend to feel defiant as well as sheepish?

16. Do you tend to venture into company only if you have someone to look after you?

17. Do you like to keep a reserve close relationship going just in case your principal relationship falters?

18. Have you gone off with someone else's partner more than once?

19. Do you tend to find someone else to be close to you when your primary partner is away even for a short time?

20. Have you ever had three or more sexual relationships going at the same period of time?

21. Have you ever tried to prove to yourself that you are self-sufficient and can do without close relationships?

22. Are you aware from your own experience that each of your relationships tends to follow a pattern that results in disillusion that there will ever be anyone who really cares for you sufficiently?

15

23. Are you afraid that life will be pointless if you do not have a particularly close relationship?

24. Do you frequently make relationships with people who are less strong willed than you?

25. Do you tend to find a new close relationship within days or weeks of the failure of a previous one?

26. Do you find that other people tend to express progressively more concern about your relationships?

27. Have you ever done something deliberately damaging to yourself even though you have only just recovered from the previous episode of self-inflicted damage?

28. Do you find that you almost pride yourself on not begin able to look after yourself without other people to care for you?

29. Do you find that all of these questions are perfectly straight-forward and none of them a bit strange?

30. Would you instinctively understand someone who answered yes to *all* of these questions?

(viii) **Sex**

1. Do you feel an almost overwhelming sense of excitement when there is the prospect of a new sexual partner?

2. Do you get irritable and impatient in a relationship if it does not progress to sexual activity within the first few meetings?

3. Would it be more painful to give up promiscuous sex than to give up a close friendship?

4. Do you not infrequently find that making a sexual conquest causes you to lose interest in that partner and lead you to begin looking for another?

5. Do you pride yourself on the speed with which you can get to have sex with someone and find that sex with a complete stranger is particularly stimulating?

6. Do you find masturbation by yourself more stimulating than with a partner?

7. Do you often use sex simply to help you get to sleep and not because you really care for your partner?

8. Do you particularly enjoy experimenting with new sexual positions or practices as frequently as possible so that you tend to get bored with standard positions or practices?

9. Do you tend to think of sexual activity not so much as a shared activity with a regular partner but as a reward that you deserve because of stress that you endure?

10. Have you ever had sex with an animal or had some other form of sex that might generally be considered to be disgusting?

11. Have you ever felt in a strange way that you only become a "real" person when you are having sex?

12. Have you ever had voluntary sex with someone you dislike?

13. Do you tend to ensure that you have sex of one kind or another rather than wait for your regular partner to be available again after illness or absence?

14. Do you tend to use sex as both a comfort and strength even when you are not feeling particularly sexually stimulated?

15. When you have definitely had sexual activity at the expense of someone else's feelings, do you tend to feel defiant as well as slightly disappointed with yourself?

16. When you have a regular partner do you tend also to masturbate on your own in secret?

17. After a time of separation do you tend to grab the first available opportunity to have sex rather than wait until later in the day when it may be more relaxed and mutually enjoyable?

18. Have you ever had repeated affairs even though you had a regular relationship?

19. Do you find it difficult to pass over an opportunity for casual or illicit sex?

20. Do you find that the physical health of your partner has tended not to influence your desire for or insistence upon sex?

21. Have you ever tried to prove to yourself that you are not promiscuous by giving up new conquests for a week or month or more?

22. Are you aware from your own experience that, once in any day you set your intention to have sex, you find it difficult to focus on anything else?

23. Are you afraid that life will become unbearably dull and boring as you get older and sex becomes less frequent?

24. Do you tend to change partners if sex becomes repetitive?

25. Have you ever had three or more regular sexual relationships at the same time?

26. Has anyone else expressed repeated serious concern over your sexual behaviour?

17

27. Would you take up an opportunity to have sex despite having just had it with someone else?

28. Do you consider someone who has recently been jilted or bereaved to be fair game?

29. Do you find that all of these questions are perfectly straight-forward and none of them disturbing or strange?

30. Do you feel that you would instinctively understand someone who answered yes to *all* of these questions?

(ix) Shopping and Spending and Stealing

1. Do you feel a sense of increased tension and excitement when you plan to go out shopping or plan to spend or steal?

2. Do you get excessively irritable and impatient if there is a queue at the cash desk or if you have to go somewhere else to get what you want?

3. Would it be more painful for you to hand over your purchasing ability (cash, cheques, cards etc) to someone else than to give up a close friendship?

4. Do you not infrequently buy or steal so many goods (groceries, sweets, household goods, books etc) that it would take you a month or more to get through them?

5. Have you often bought or stolen goods that you do not really want at all?

6. Are you uncomfortable shopping with other people because you feel that it restricts your freedom?

7. Do you go shopping or stealing (in the High Street or in a Garden Centre or anywhere) to calm your nerves?

8. Do you particularly enjoy bargains so that you often finish up with more than you need?

9. Do you think of buying or stealing things not so much as a means of providing necessities but more as a reward that you deserve for stresses that you endure?

10. Have you often bought or stolen something simply because you happened to have the money or opportunity?

11. Do you feel in a strange way that you really become "yourself" when you are shopping, spending or stealing?

12. Have you repeatedly bought from catalogues or advertisements even though you have been disappointed with goods previously purchased through those same channels?

13. Do you prefer always to keep your supplies "topped up" (in case of natural disaster or war) rather than let your stocks run low?

14. Do you tend to use shopping, spending or stealing as both a comfort and strength even when you do not particularly need anything?

15. When you have definitely bought too much or been on a stealing spree, do you tend to feel defiant as well as sheepish?

16. When you are shopping or spending along with family members or friends or others do you tend to disguise the full extent of your purchases?

17. Would you tend to buy something you really do not want rather than take another half an hour in order to get something you really do want?

18. Have you ever regularly stolen or helped yourself to other people's goods or services even when you had enough of your own or enough money to buy your own?

19. Do you find it difficult to leave any money in your purse or wallet when you go out shopping at Christmas or in your favourite type of shop or organisation?

20. Do you find that running out of available money is often irrelevant in deciding when to stop shopping or spending?

21. Have you ever cut up your credit cards or given back your check book to prove to yourself that you can live within your means when you try?

22. Are you aware from your own experience that once you start buying or stealing it is difficult to stop?

23. Are you afraid that life will become excessively boring and dull if you have to live within a fixed budget?

24. Do you tend to go shopping "just in case" you might see something you want?

25. Have you ever had three or more personal bank accounts or general credit facilities at the same time?

26. Has anyone else expressed repeated serious concern over your stealing or over your unreliability with shopping or spending?

27. Would you take up an opportunity to go out shopping or stealing even though you have only just got back from such an activity?

28. Do you find it difficult to throw away old things and often take in other people's throwouts just in case they might come in handy?

29. Do you find that all of these questions are perfectly straight-forward and none of them a bit strange?

30. Do you feel that you would instinctively understand someone who answered yes to *all* of these questions?

(x) Exercise

1. Do you feel a particular sense of tension and excitement when you are about to take exercise?

2. Do you get irritable and impatient if for some reason you are delayed for ten minutes?

3. Would it be more painful to give up exercise than to give up a close friendship?

4. Do you not infrequently get yourself so tired with exercise that you find it difficult to walk or to climb upstairs?

5. Do you tend to grab at any chance of doing exercise of some kind or other?

6. Do you almost prefer to exercise alone rather than in company?

7. Have you often taken exercise just to tire yourself sufficiently for sleep or to calm your nerves?

8. Do you particularly enjoy getting wringing wet with sweat?

9. Do you tend to think of exercise not so much as a means of keeping reasonably fit but as a reward that you deserve because of stress you endure?

10. Have you ever taken exercise despite a fracture or severe sprain?

11. Do you feel in a strange way that you only really become "yourself" when you are exercising?

12. Have you ever taken exercise just for the sake of it even though you actively disliked the particular sport or company?

13. Do you prefer to take exercise several times a day?

14. Do you tend to use exercise as both a comfort and strength even when you are perfectly fit and do not need any more?

15. When you have definitely strained yourself from overexer-cising, do you tend to feel defiant as well as disappointed with yourself?

16. When you are exercising in company do you tend to disguise from others just how much exercise you generally take?

17. Would you take some form of exercise immediately at the time you expected to take exercise rather than wait half an hour for what you really wanted to do?

18. Have you ever regularly stolen other people's sports equipment even though you had plenty of money to get your own or booked up courts for more than your own real needs even though this may prevent some other people from getting any access at all?

19. Do you find it difficult to stop exercising before the allotted time is up even though something important may need to be done?

20. Do you find that being worn out is often irrelevant in deciding when to stop exercising?

21. Have you ever given up regular exercise just to prove to yourself that you are not addicted to it?

22. Are you aware from your own experience that once you start exercising in any day you find it difficult to stop?

23. Are you afraid that life will become excessively dull and boring or that you will put on excessive amounts of weight if you significantly cut down the level of exercise you take?

24. Do you tend to take sports clothes and equipment with you mostly wherever you go "just in case" the opportunity for exercise turns up?

25. Have you ever played three or more competition standard sports regularly at the same time of year?

26. Has anyone else expressed repeated serious concern about the level of exercise you take?

27. Would you respond positively to an unexpected invitation for exercise despite having just finished your regular exercise?

28. Do you regularly specifically attempt to work off the extra calories of a meal by doing extra exercise?

29. Do you find that all of these questions are perfectly straightforward and none of them a bit strange?

30. Do you feel that you would instinctively understand someone who answered yes to *all* of these questions?

(xi) **Prescription Drugs**

Drugs of choice – tranquillisers, antidepressants, painkillers, cough mixtures and cold cures, sleeping tablets, slimming pills, antihistamines.

21

WARNING: Do not suddenly stop taking any medication that you have used regularly: withdrawal symptoms may be very severe. Discuss your concerns with your doctor.

1. Do you feel a sense of increased tension or awareness when it is coming to the time when you normally take your medication?

2. Do you tend to get concerned, irritable or impatient if there is a delay of ten minutes or more beyond the time when you anticipated receiving your medication, obtaining your prescription or having it filled?

3. Would you be more concerned at the prospect of having your prescription slowly but progressively reduced to zero than at the prospect of losing a close friendship?

4. Do you find that your previous doses or medications are no longer fully successful in controlling your symptoms?

5. Do you sometimes take an additional dose if you are concerned by the prospect of particular stress?

6. Do you feel cheated and feel that your problems have been under-valued if someone close to you suggests that you do not really need your medication?

7. Do you tend to take an extra dose if you wake up in the middle of the night?

8. Do you prefer to feel no stress even if it means that you also feel less spontaneous happiness?

9. Do you feel that you have greater stresses, or less natural capacity to cope with them, than other people have?

10. If you dropped your last tablet in the lavatory pan would you fish it out?

11. Would you continue, or have you continued, taking your present medication even if it reduces your sexual urges and capacity?

12. If you were away from home and had forgotten your tablets would you take a prescription medication that someone else uses, even if you have not tried it previously and are not absolutely sure that it is prescribed for the same problem as yours?

13. Do you like to be absolutely regular in the timing of taking your medication?

14. Do you tend to us your medication as both a comfort and strength?

15. When you return to using medication after a time of abstinence do you tend to feel defiant as well as disappointed in yourself?

16. Do you have a second doctor (not known to the first) prepared to give you medication?

17. If, for some reason, you miss a dose, would you "make it up to yourself" by taking an extra dose later on?

18. Do you feel threatened if someone close to you tries to supervise or reduce your medication *and* have you ever stolen or lied in order to protect your reserve supply?

19. If your supply was being strictly controlled, would you hang on to some old tablets even if they were definitely beyond their expiry date?

20. Do you continue to take medication because you find it helps you, even though the original stresses for which the medication was prescribed has resolved?

21. Have you tried to prove that you are not addicted by giving up your medication for a week, a month or more?

22. Are you aware from your own experience that once you return to taking your medication after a period of abstinence you very quickly return to the same dosage or even more than before?

23. Are you *consciously* determined – and generally proud of – your ability to control your use of medications?

24. Do you sometimes take more than the prescribed doses when you have been given more than was necessary for the number of days until your next prescription?

25. Have you repeatedly cancelled social engagements, lost two or more jobs or failed to keep regular appointments or arrangements because you have not felt able to cope with life, even despite taking your medication?

26. Has anyone else expressed repeated serious concern about your use of prescription medicines?

27. Has a doctor or anyone else ever commented that he or she would be knocked out by a fraction of the doses that you take regularly?

28. Do you find that your alcohol or food consumption goes up when you are off medication?

29. Do you find that all of these questions are perfectly straightforward and none of them a bit strange?

30. Do you feel that you would instinctively understand someone who answered yes to *all* of these questions?

22. Are you aware from your own experience that some substances act as "trigger" foods so that, once started, it is difficult to control further eating?

23. Are you afraid that you will put on excessive amounts of weight if you give up smoking or using laxatives or appetite suppressants or self-induced vomiting or exercising or give up strict control of food intake?

24. Do you actively prefer restaurants where they serve large portions, even when you are not concerned with the cost?

25. Have you ever had three or more different sizes of clothes in your adult, non-pregnant, wardrobe?

26. Has anyone else expressed repeated serious concern over your eating habits, body weight or shape?

27. Would you eat a full meal in response to an unexpected invitation, despite having already eaten a full meal?

28. Would you think it wasteful if any of the dishes in an Indian or Chinese meal are left unfinished and would you therefore finish them even if you are not hungry *and* are other people's leftovers generally fair game for you to finish off?

29. Do you find that all of these questions are perfectly straight-forward and none of them a bit strange?

30. Do you feel that you would instinctively understand someone who answered yes to *all* of these questions?

(b) *Starving*

1. In a restaurant or even at home do you not infrequently try to persuade other people to choose dishes that you know you would like even though you yourself would probably refuse to eat them?

2. Do you get irritable and impatient at mealtimes if someone tries to persuade you to eat something?

3. Would it be more painful for you to give up sugar and white flour – and therefore everything that contains sugar and white flour – than to give up a close friendship?

4. Do you not infrequently chew something and then take it out of your mouth and throw it away?

5. When you swallow food does it often tend to make you feel unhappy, queasy, and bloated?

6. On the occasions that you eat at all, do you prefer to eat alone rather than in company?

7. Have you often tried to empty your body of as much fluid as possible so that you feel at peace before going to bed at night?

8. Do you *particularly* enjoy eating raw vegetables and also salty or sour things?

9. Do you tend to think of losing weight and changing your body shape as a reward that you deserve because of stress you endure?

10. Have you ever had a list of so many things that you dare not eat, that there is very little left that you can eat?

11. Do you feel in a strange way that you are "understoood" by food and that you have a particular intimate relationship with it and that you only become a "real" person when eating particular foods or abstaining altogether from eating?

12. Does the smell of some food make you wish that you could eat it like other people do but do you nonetheless find that you cannot bring yourself to do so?

13. Do you not uncommonly find that you are no longer hungry even if you have not eaten for a day or two or even more?

14. Do you tend to reduce your intake of liquids in order to give yourself a feeling of comfort and strength?

15. When you do eat something reasonably substantial do you tend to feel disappointed or even angry with yourself as well as slightly relieved?

16. When you are eating in company do you tend to time your eating as a form of strategy so that others are not really aware of precisely how little you are eating?

17. Have you often simply absented yourself at mealtimes or said, substantially untruthfully, that you have already eaten?

18. Have you ever regularly stolen or helped yourself to other people's sweets or food even though you had enough money to buy your own?

19. Do you find it difficult to finish everything on your plate, almost regardless of how little you put on it in the first place?

20. Do you hate feeling full and find it virtually impossible to eat any more when you have that feeling?

21. Do you find that you sometimes lose weight even though you were not specifically intending to do so?

22. Are you aware from your own experience that some substances act as "trigger" foods so that, once started, it is difficult to control further eating?

23. Are you afraid that you will put on an *excessive* amount of weight if you give up smoking or using laxatives or appetite supressants or self-induced vomiting or exercising or give up strict control of food intake?

24. If you go out in company to a restaurant do you prefer simply to drink some tea or coffee or have a diet drink while everyone else is eating?

25. Have you ever had three or more different sizes of clothes in your adult, non-pregnant wardrobe.

26. Has anyone else expressed repeated, serious, concern over your eating habits, body weight or shape?

27. If you find that you have put on some weight do you commonly stop eating altogether for a day or two?

28. If you do eat in company do you like to be with special friends or family members whom you can rely upon to finish off some foods for you?

29. Do you find that all of these questions are perfectly straight-forward and none of them a bit strange?

30. Do you feel you would instinctively understand someone who answered yes to *all* of these questions?

CHAPTER Two

Interpreting the answers to the PROMIS Addiction Questionnaires

A positive answer to *ANY* question may just possibly be an indication of a compulsive or addictive disorder.

This may seem excessively severe but the questions are specifically designed to look for compulsive or addictive characteristics. Someone who has no form of addictive disease will most commonly answer "no" to all the questions. Conversely, however, there may be false positive answers from some people who may be over-anxious by nature or who may find questionnaires confusing or imprecise.

It is important to remember that the primary psycho-pathology of any addictive disease is "denial". Thus, as mentioned in the Introduction, the prime psychological feature of addictive disease is that it tells the sufferer that he or she does not have it. For example, the sufferers from alcoholism often believe that they may have problems with stress or depression but no real problem with alcohol and they may sometimes be supported in this view by their families and even by their doctors. So also the sufferers from drug addiction may have given up drugs many times, thereby spuriously "proving" to themselves that they are not addicted – but never wondering how it is that they are nonetheless repeatedly drawn back to one mood-altering substance or another. Similarly, the sufferers from eating disorders may accept that they have problems with body weight or shape but adamantly refuse to consider that their relationship with food may be basically compulsive or addictive in nature.

Thus, in questionnaires designed by people who think in terms of "drunkeness" and of "safe" units of alcohol consumed and of "sensible drinking programmes", the sufferer from alcoholism may happily tick off all the "no" answers. Not only do those questionnaires tend to lack insight into the nature of addictive disease but also there may be little awareness of the sheer intensity of denial that can result in the sufferer from alcoholism simply not making any mental connection between the alcohol consumed and the various damaging events that are in fact direct consequences of alcoholism.

Similarly, as another example, the sufferers from eating disorders may blithely tick off all the "no" answers in questionnaires designed by people who are not aware that the Eating Disorders form part of the spectrum of addictive disease.

Despite denial, the sufferers from any form of addictive disease often have an inner fear of insanity or uncontrolability in the awareness that particular substances or behaviours are beginning to control many aspects of life and not simply the need for biochemical fuel or normal function. Coupled to this is the desparate fear that there appears to be no way out – all methods of external control have failed. Furthermore, the strength of the addictive relationship with the particular substances or patterns of behaviour may be so great as to make the prospect of doing without them "unthinkable". As a result of a combination of these various factors, the sufferer may put down a whole row of "no" answers even when knowing inwardly that some, or even all, of the answers should have been "yes". Consequently, if even one positive answer slips through the defensive net it may be an indication that there is need for further assessment by counselling staff specialising in addictive disease.

It may be most helpful to go through the PROMIS Addiction Questionnaires with someone else. Many of the questions are subjective, answerable only by the sufferer, but some have objective features and could be answered by anyone who knows the sufferer well. However, sometimes that other person may be too close to be able to see clearly and may have intense emotional commitment to concepts and potential "solutions" of his or her own and therefore be unable to give a truly objective assessment. Best of all is to go through the questionnaires with a counsellor specialising in addictive disease.

The general practical interpretation of the PROMIS Addiction Questionnaires is as follows:

i. Zero positive answers indicates no addictive disease.

ii. One to five positive answers indicates the possibility of addictive disease of some kind but probably no significant addiction in this specific area.

iii. Six to nine positive answers indicates a greater possibility of addictive disease of some kind and quite possibly in this specific area. Further assessment will be necessary.

iv. Ten to nineteen positive answers indicates addictive disease of some kind and also a definite cross-addiction in this specific area. These sufferers will need to deal with this disorder as well as deal with what they considered to be their primary addiction involving their drug or behaviour of choice. Failure to deal with this additional specific area will result in recovery being stunted so that there is a high risk of relapse.

v. Twenty or more positive answers indicates addictive disease in this specific area with this primary drug or behaviour of choice. These sufferers may or may not have other cross addictions of equal or lesser importance.

What is the significance of each individual question in the PROMIS Addiction Questionnaire?

Question 1. (Physical sense of increased tension) looks for preoccupation with the specific "drug of choice" that is a feature for each sufferer from addictive disease. There tends to be anticipatory excitement for sufferers from any form of addictive disease when contemplating use of their own specific "drug or behaviour of choice".

Question 2. (Irritable and impatient over ten minutes delay) The "theme song" of any addictive disease is "I want what I want when I want it and I want it *now* ". A wait of half an hour would try anybody's patience but ten minutes is socially acceptable to all but the sufferers from addiction.

Question 3. (Pain of giving up the substance or behaviour of choice rather than a close friendship) looks at the intensity of the relationship with the primary drug of choice. For example, for someone with an eating disorder, sugar is the exact equivalent of alcohol for the sufferer from alcoholism or of cocaine, cannabis, heroin, amphetamines, solvents, Valium or some other specific mood-altering drug of choice, for sufferers from drug addiction. Similarly, it is the equivalent of the crucial first card or spin or "go" for the compulsive gambler or risk taker, the first cigarette for the nicotine addict, the first cup of tea, chocolate or glass of cola or lemondade for the caffeine addict and so on.

The intensity of the relationship is something only another addict can understand. Frequently, well-meaning friends or helpers may say "Well, I gave up smoking (or whatever) . . ." without any insight into the fact that for them smoking (or whatever) was simply a habit and not the truly addictive process that some other smokers (or users) find they simply *cannot* give up, however hard they try. Indeed, many sufferers are themselves unaware of the extreme difficulty of totally giving up their drug or behaviour of choice until they try to do so.

Given the choice of "drugs" or home, an addict will commonly choose drugs. The relationship between an addict of any kind and his or her drug of choice is the primary relationship of life. It is clung to until almost, or even absolutely, everything else is destroyed. The relationship is stronger than many human relationships and is so special (in a way that other people find strange and upsetting) that an addict may say that he or she only feels "understood" by his or her substance or behaviour of choice. *This* is the intensity of addiction – the feeling that human relationships may come and go but the relationship with the drug or behaviour of choice is intensely personal and private, special and different.

Question 4. (Initial use stimulating the desire for more) illustrates the impossibility of satisfying a craving. The first "dose" in any day may or may not trigger a binge. This can be very confusing for all manner of addicts – the first use does *not* always trigger an uncontrolled response. But it *may* do so and, in time, in recovery from addiction, the recovering person learns not to risk the first use in any day.

In all addictions, there is a great deal more to recovery than this first step of physical abstinence but this first step is nonetheless essential.

Question 5. (Gulping or grabbing) illustrates the use of the substance or behaviour of choice for its emotional effect to fill an "inner void".

Question 6. (Preference for use alone) again illustrates the primary nature of the relationship between an addict and his or her substance or behaviour of choice.

Question 7. (Use to sleep or to provide stimulation or to calm nerves) particularly shows the level of pre-occupation that is part of addictive disease. It is not simply that the sufferer is being cautious in planning ahead, it is more, for example, that he or she fears or may even *hope* to wake up in the middle of the night, but at least will have a further "dose" readily available.

Question 8. (Particular enjoyment of strong dose or stimulus) demonstrates that sufferers from addictive disease know exactly where the greatest mood-altering response may be obtained.

Question 9. (Rewards for stress) particularly illustrates the medicinal, tranquillising effects so that the substance or behaviour of choice is used in response to stress rather than for the original, generally understood, purpose. Many people "reward" themselves with an occasional meal or drink without this implying that they are suffering from an eating disorder or from alcoholism, but they would normally eat and drink in response to hunger and thirst and would develop other forms of response to stress – such as tackling the source of specific stresses. For the addict there is no great advantage in resolving particular stresses – that would close down a principal rationalisation for continuing to use the substance or behaviour of addiction. For the addict the substance or behaviour of addiction is always a reward in some way and therefore it becomes the favoured reward, regardless of its relevance to other circumstances such as hunger or thirst or emotional pain.

Question 10. (Use despite disgust) looks again at the sufferer's use of the tranquillising effect of the substance or behaviour of choice.

Question 11. (Being a "real" person when using the substance or behaviour of choice) illustrates the crude intimacy of the relationship between the sufferer and his or her substance or behaviour of choice.

Question 12. (Use of any available alternative) again emphasises that *now* is what counts.

Question 13. (Regular supply throughout the day) again illustrates the tranquillising effect. Maintenance doses may only be small but they keep the tranquillising effect "topped-up".

Question 14. (Use for comfort and strength) particularly illustrates that the use is for emotional rather than physical reasons.

Question 15. (Co-existent feeling of defiance and awkwardness after exccessive use) is particularly important because it demonstrates the difference between the addictive disease itself and the suffering individual that it inflicts. The individual is pathetically disappointed whereas the disease, as an alien parasite affecting mind and behaviour, is defiant. The capacity to see this differentiation between the suffering individual and the afflicting addictive disease is crucial to the disease concept of addiction. Traditionally, addiction tends to be thought of as the product of weak will and of disturbance in psychological and social background. The disease concept, adopted in Minnesota Method treatment centres based upon the principles of Alcoholics Anonymous and other Anonymous Fellowships, holds that background is not a primary determinant and that strong rather than weak will is a cause of problems and, further, that addictive disease affects some people but not others and that it is not the fault of the sufferer nor within his or her control.

Question 16. (Strategy when in company) is another crucially important question because it demonstrates the sufferer's self obsession and the consequent need to be aware of what everyone else around him or her is doing. The drug or behaviour or choice is the primary subject of relationship that rivets his or her attention, not the people. The perceived need to disguise from others (commonly unsuccessfully) the exact relationship with the substance or behaviour of choice is part of the delusion of addictive disease. In the first place, other people are not particularly interested and, secondly, they are not fooled anyway.

Question 17. (Keeping topped up) illustrates the obsession with predictable regularity of supply. The unpredictable is very unsettling and therefore precautions may be taken.

Question 18. (Stealing or helping yourself) shows the disease protecting its supply routes. In all forms of addictive disease, it shows the distressing disparity between values and behaviour. However, as the addictive disease progressively worsens and behaviour gets worse along with it, the gap between values and behaviour becomes unbridgeable. At this point there is a serious risk of suicide. Significant numbers of sufferers from addictive disease opt for that tragic way out because they have no concept of any alternative solution. Alternatively, they adjust their values to comply with their behaviour and the trail of progressive degradation continues.

Question 19. (Difficulty in leaving some) shows again that normal feelings of satisfaction are not relevant to the amount of substance consumed or behaviour used.

Question 20. (Continuing use despite standard indications of sufficiency) is the same as question 19 expressed in more explicit form.

Question 21. ("Proof" to self that the substance or behaviour can be given up) illustrates the impossibility of "control" solutions to the compulsions of addictive disease.

Question 22. (Using more than intended) is asking the specific question about trigger substances or behaviour. Many sufferers would answer "no" to this question not only because it never occured to them to look but also because the disease does not want them to look and therefore, in subconscious denial, they simply do not see. Again, it may seem positively wierd to refer to the disease as if it had an entity of its own, with its own mind and behaviour, – but addictive disease does indeed behave like that.

Question 23. (Fear of loss of control) is a crucial question for any sufferers from addictive disease. Any of the processes referred to can be simply methods of trying to pre-empt or control the consequences of addictive behaviour.

Question 24. (Increasing supply at reduced cost) again looks at the adjustment of values to comply with behaviour and also looks at the generally high capacity that sufferers have for their substance or behaviour of choice.

Question 25. (Continuing use despite damaging consequences) looks pragmatically at the failure of "control" solutions.

Question 26. (Concern of other people) attempts to obtain some objectivity but the disease may quickly rationalise it away by making out, in the sufferer's mind, that the *other* person has problems of perception.

Question 27. (Going round again for a second time) looks at the higher capacity than others, at the irrelevance of normal stimuli, at the "triggering'' effect and at the protection of supply. It is such an obvious question that it risks getting a flat denial even when the sufferer remembers specific occasions only too well. The shame of admitting it may be just too great. On the other hand, when the suffering is so great as to cause desperation, this question may tip the balance into giving up the struggle of denial.

Question 28. (Higher capacity than others) looks at the increased capacity that comes with practice. This increased capacity is gradually lost as the addictive disease progresses.

Question 29. (Questions straightforward rather than strange) is an attempt to force the sufferer to come down on one side or the other. The dilemma is that if he or she says that some of the questions are strange (as the disease would wish and as other people would genuinely say) then that would be the ultimate self-denial and giving in to the disease. As the sufferer progresses through the questions he or she will secretly have realised that they are the ''right'' questions: that they could only have been asked by people who have had first hand experience of an addictive disease. Thus, there is a stark choice: go with the questioner or go with the disease. Superficially it may appear that someone with a kindly disposition or detached clinical interest might answer ''yes'' in the hope of telling the truth but at the same time not *really* being disloyal to the disease, the primary subject of relationship in life. But the trap for the disease is sprung: nobody but another sufferer would think that *all* the questions were reasonable and *none* of them a bit strange.

Question 30. (Instinctive understanding of someone who answered yes to all questions) tries to cement the relationship with the questioner. The loneliness of the inner awareness – that other people find some or even all of the sufferer's behaviour to be strange or bizarre or weird – can at last begin to be dispelled by sharing it with one other human being. Having demonstrated that *one* other person (the questioner) has shared the same thoughts and fears, humiliations and degradations and yet somehow has survived, then the sufferer may come to believe that perhaps there is hope after all.

What are the common characteristics in any form of addictive disease?

Dr Richard Heilman of the Hazelden Foundation in Minnesota identifies the following eight characteristics:

1. *Pre-occupation*
   Looking forward to use. Planning life around it. Making plans for specific times of abstinence.

2. *Use alone*
   Use in private is just as comfortable (or even more so) as use in company

3. *Use for effect*
   A special "lift", "feel" or "buzz" is sought from the substance or behaviour, rather than simply the taste or the normal consequence that is experienced by others.

4. *Use as a medicine*
   The substance or behaviour may be used to help to relax or to help sleep or to provide stimulation or, most of all, to suppress uncomfortable emotional feelings.

5. *Protection of supply*
   The substance or behaviour is used to smother disturbed feelings. Its supply (or the money, time and other things required for it) tends to be disproportionately carefully protected.

6. *Using more than planned*
   Incapacity to predict what will happen after the use of the substance or behaviour is started on any occasion.

7. *Increased capacity*
   Greater capacity than others to use a particular substance or behaviour. In the late stages of the disease this "tolerance" is lost.

8. *Memory blankouts*
   The memory functions of the brain may cease to function when it is intoxicated or otherwise overloaded. This may lead to loss of awareness that conversations or events ever took place. (This "denial" needs to be exposed by other people by *not* covering up the damaging consequences of use of the substance or behaviour).

Reflecting now upon the PROMIS Addiction Questionnaires, it can be seen that these same characteristics (excluding the last) flow through each Questionnaire. Some questions look at one particular characteristic whereas other questions look at several. There is considerable overlap between groups of questions concerning particular characteristics but, in simple terms, they correspond approximately as follows:-

Questions 1 to 5: Preoccupation

Questions 6 and 7: Use alone

Questions 7 and 8: Use as a medicine

Questions 9 to 12: Using for effect

Questions 13 to 18: Protection of supply

Questions 19 to 23: Using more than planned

Questions 24 to 28: Higher capacity than others

The eighth characteristic – memory blankouts – has been omitted from the PROMIS Addiction Questionnaires despite the fact that some sufferers describe this experience. The difficulty is in formulating a question that clearly delineates all sufferers from addictive disease from other people. True blackouts involving complete loss of memory for a part of an hour, or even for a whole evening or more, are very much a specific characteristic of addictive disease. Memory lapses, on precisely what was said or done at a particular brief moment in a party or other social occasion, can happen to anybody.

Dr Heilman holds that addictive disease can only be diagnosed with certainty if four of these eight criteria are present. However, this really applies to live interviews with addiction counsellors rather than to written questionnaires which are easily fudged. The PROMIS Addiction Questionnaires should therefore ideally be administered by an addiction counsellor who would put in further spontaneous questions in order to clarify the presence or absence of specific characteristics. Under those criteria it would possibly be reasonable to expect positive answers in four separate groups of questions corresponding to Dr Heilman's addiction characteristics.

However, it should be emphasised that the disease will split as many hairs as possible, as well as flatly deny the obvious. After further interview with an addiction counsellor it may be recommended that a period of in-patient assessment alongside other sufferers from addictive disease would be the best method of being sure of diagnosis. The sum capacity of a group of sufferers to discern whether a newcomer truly belongs in the group or not is a far more accurate diagnostic tool than any written questionnaire or assessment by any individual addiction counsellor.

The Target of Addictive Disease

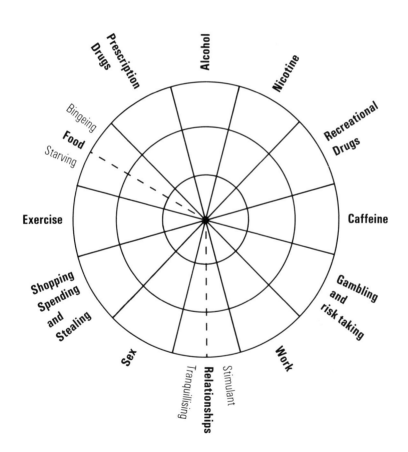

Imagine that your addictive disease has you "in its sights". The twelve questionnaires will have shown you where it is most likely to strike. Draw in on this target the number of positive answers that you have in each questionnaire and you will see the pattern of your own addictive disease and know where your future risks lie.

You will find that your addictive tendency will most probably (but not inevitably) be clustered in one part of the target. Each sufferer is individual in the over all pattern of his or her addictive disease. Nonetheless, there are common cross addictions closely associated with each particular form of addiction. The whole target is made up from the continuum of close associations.

It seems to me that the specific addictions on the left side of the target tend to be tranquillising in their effect, while those on the right side tend to be stimulant. But this is not an absolute rule. For example, alcohol has a short term tranquillising effect but longer term stimulant effect. Equally, it may be that other addictive substances and behaviours may be stimulant in some people while primarily tranquillising in others. Nonetheless, in summary, I simply observe the following:

(i) cross addictions tend to go in clusters.

(ii) the various addictions appear to form a continuum as illustrated on this target.

(iii) the addictions on the left side of the target tend to be tranquillising in their effect while those on the right side tend to be stimulant.

(iv) Adding up the total number of positive answers in *all* the PROMIS Addiction Questionnaires may give an indication of the overall severity of an individual's addictive disease relative to that of other sufferers.

The explanations for these observations and for the reasons why individuals have specific patterns of cross-addiction are beyond me. Also, I do not know how stable these patterns of cross-addiction may be in any individual over a lifetime, nor do I know any patterns of inheritance of cross-addiction.

I mention these observations not with any scientific certainty but more in the hope of stimulating further investigation.

The "Family Disease"

Commonly in science a substance will be present along with its isomer or mirror image, or two different species will live in symbiosis, mutually dependent upon each other. Addictive disease also follows these principles. The "Family Disease" is the term given to the tendency (which is itself addictive in its behavioural pattern) that some people have towards destructive self-denial and towards caretaking for sufferers from primary addictive disease. Thus, the "drugs" of addictive "Family Disease" are self denial and caretaking.

Self denial and caretaking for others may, at first sight, appear to be positive, kind and considerate attributes. This may be so. However, they may be most destructive when taken to extremes and used primarily to satisfy the emotional needs of the family member himself or herself, regardless of whether the denial or caretaking actually does help the primary sufferer or anyone else.

The following questionnaire for the "Family Disease" is based upon exactly similar questions to those for the various primary addictions. The "Family Disease" may also be genetically inherited as it also appears to run in families, to follow the same progressive pattern of destruction as any primary addiction, and to get better in an appropriate Anonymous Fellowship for family members. Moreover, the tendency towards the behavioural characteristics in family members may *precede* awareness of primary addictive disease in a close family member or friend.

It would be nice to think that if one inherited both a primary addiction and the "Family Disease" then they would cancel each other out. This may happen in some people. Who knows? However, it also appears that some people get both primary addictive disease and the "Family Disease". These people tend to be referred to, somewhat less than ingenuously, as "double winners".

A particular risk of "double winners" is when they come to work as professional counsellors or health care professionals in any sphere. This combination of primary addictive disease and "Family Disease" can be potentially most damaging in the professional field of counselling for addictive disease itself. Most addiction counsellors are selected for training if they are themselves in recovery (for a least two years) from primary addictive disease. If, at the same time, they also have the "Family Disease" then they can get themselves and their patients into a dreadful mess very quickly as a result of self denial and caretaking. To use a common expression, they "burn out".

It is vital therefore that anyone working, or hoping to work, in the field of addiction counselling should be assessed for "Family Disease" and, if appropriate, seek help through the Family Fellowships. The probability, bearing in mind that addictive disease itself runs in families, is that the counsellor or prospective counsellor already has direct family qualifications for membership of a Family Fellowship and, failing that, will have more than enough close friends with primary addictive disease to make up the alternative qualification for membership of the Family Fellowships.

It should be emphasised, in parenthesis, that Family Fellowships are for *personal* recovery rather than professional preparation or qualification. Nonetheless, the result of that personal recovery will profoundly help the professional capacity whereas its absence could cause a great deal of damage.

The constructive action for a family member is to learn what is truly helpful rather than what "ought" to be helpful. The constructive action for a professional is to *be* professional and not to be destroyed by over-zealous "caring".

A positive answer to any of the following questions may be cause for concern:

Behaviours of choice in the "Family Disease" are "Self-denial" of one's own feelings and needs and addictive "Caretaking" for the feelings and needs of others. As with other forms of addictive relationships, the "Family Disease" may present in dominant (stimulant) or submissive (tranquillising) forms.

(a) Dominant (Stimulant) Family Disease

1. Do you feel a sense of almost overwhelming excitement when you take on a new prospect or opportunity for helping someone else?

2. Do you get irritable when there is nobody around for you to help or when those who are around do not appear to appreciate the help that you have to offer?

3. Would it be more painful for you to give up the sense of being needed for other people than to give up a close friendship?

4. Do you find life rather empty when someone for whom you have been caring gets better *and* have you at times felt almost resentful when you are no longer needed?

5. Do you tend to grab at the chance to look after people so that they may sometimes say that they find this overwhelming and ask you to get off their backs?

6. Do you prefer to look after people on your own rather than as part of a team and do you tend to believe that you have the power – or can acquire the knowledge – specifically required to help a particular individual or even several people all at once.

7. Do you find that looking after other people tends to settle your own nerves?

8. Do you feel particularly worthy if you give up your own free time or holiday in caring for other people?

9. Do you tend to think of the virtue of helping others as being its own reward, regardless of the personal cost to yourself?

10. Have you ever utterly shamed or debased yourself in an attempt to help or encourage someone else?

11. Do you feel in a strange way that you only become a "real" person when you are tidying up the physical, emotional and social messes made by people for whom you care?

12. Have you ever done things that you actively dislike or disagree with but felt you *had* to do in the service of others and to protect them from potentially damaging consequences of their own actions.

13. Do you find that you tend to adopt a self denying and caretaking role in many of your relationships?

14. Do you tend to use your self denial and caretaking for others as both a comfort and strength for yourself?

15. When you have definitely taken too much responsibility for someone else, regardless of the cost to yourself, do you tend to feel defiant as well as sheepish?

16. When you are living or working alongside others do you tend to disguise from them how much you caretake for someone in that environment who, in your own view, is particularly needy?

17. If you have half an hour on your hands, would you tend to find something to read or to do that enhances your capacity to protect a particular individual from the damaging consequences of his or her own actions?

18. Have you ever regularly given unsolicited advice to other people on how to solve their problems?

19. Do you find it difficult to leave any loose ends in a conversation in which you are trying to be helpful?

20. Do you find that there is not much left of your own personal life?

21. Have you ever tried to stop doing self denying and caretaking things altogether just to prove to yourself that it (or the person or people particularly involved) is (or are) not vital to you and not the centre of your universe?

22. Are you aware from your own experience that you frequently stay up half the night in worrying or in making plans or in having "helpful" conversations?

23. Are you afraid that you will be thought of as (and perhaps become) a callous person if you do not show your capacity for self denial and caretaking on a day-to-day basis?

24. Do you tend to go looking for someone to whom to give your particular form of help?

25. Have you ever been involved in three or more close personal relationships, each of which required your personal caretaking, all at the same time?

26. Has anyone else expressed repeated serious concern over the effect that your self denial and caretaking is having on any aspect of your own physical or emotional health?

27. Would you immediately answer a call to go back for further "helpful" conversations with someone you have only just left?

28. Have you ever held a resentment against an institution for not helping the helpers?

29. Do you find all of these questions perfectly straightforward and none of them upsetting or a bit strange?

30. Do you feel that you would instinctively understand someone who answered yes to *all* of these questions?

(b) Submissive (Tranquillising) Family Disease

1. Do you feel an almost overwhelming sense of obligation when you find a new person who needs your help or a new way of helping an existing close person?

2. Do you tend to get irritable and impatient when people look after you instead of themselves?

3. Would you tend to think that a close friendship is when you can show how much you can do to care for the other person?

4. Do you tend to give and not to count the costs even though the costs mount progressively?

5. Do you like to make yourself useful to other people even when they do not appreciate what you do?

6. Do you tend to feel surprised if someone seeks you out as a special friend?

7. Do you feel that virtue is its own reward and that you feel most in control of your feelings when you are performing services of one kind or another for someone else?

8. Do you not infrequently find that new relationships are a strain and that you are more comfortable putting more effort into an existing one?

9. Do you tend to isolate yourself from others because of your particular stresses that other people do not understand?

10. Have you, in order to help someone close to you, repeatedly done things that other people might find emotionally disturbing or disgusting?

11. Have you ever felt in a strange way that you only become a "real" person when you are performing an act of service for someone else?

12. Have you ever allowed yourself to be in a continuing close relationship with someone who damages you or repeatedly takes advantage of you in any way?

13. Do you try to avoid all risks of upsetting other people?

14. Do you tend to use isolation, or use one close relationship, as a form of comfort and strength even though this isolation or close relationship may diminish the quality and variety the rest of your life?

15. When someone has definitely taken advantage of you and you have given in far too much, do you tend to feel defiant as well as resigned?

16. When you are in company do you like to have someone you can look after or support so that little or no attention falls on you?

17. Do you tend to stick to your close relationships and find it distressing if they become relatively unpredictable?

18. Have you had three or more close relationships in which the other person takes significant advantage of you?

19. Do you tend to remain loyal and faithful regardless of what you may endure from a close relationship?

20. Have you ever had three or more people substantially dependent upon you at the same period of time?

21. Have you ever tried to prove to yourself that you can be self sufficient and not need to be heavily involved in caring for others?

22. Are you aware from your own experience that you are often so heavily involved in helping someone close to you that he or she tends to ask you to do even more?

23. Are you afraid that life will lose its point if you do not have someone close to serve?

24. Do you frequently make relationships with people whom you feel are more strong-willed than you?

25. Does it tend to take you a very long time to form really close relationships?

26. Do you find that other people tend to express concern that you are not doing sufficient for your own pleasure?

27. Do you tend to take on yet more work for someone close to you even if you have not yet finished the previous batch?

28. Do you tend to pride yourself on never being any form of burden to others?

29. Do you find that all of these questions are perfectly straightforward and none of them a bit strange?

30. Would you instinctively understand someone who answered yes to *all* of these questions?

Giving a positive answer to ANY of these questions may be an indictation of the "Family Disease". However, as with the various primary addictions, some people may give false positive answers because they may be overanxious by nature or may find questionnaires confusing or imprecise.

As a general rule the interpretation of the PROMIS Questionnaire for the "Family Disease" is as follows:-

i. Zero positive answers indicates no "Family Disease"

ii. One to nine positive answers indicates the possibility of "Family Disease" and further assessment by a counsellor specialising in addictive disease is indicated.

iii. Ten or more positive answers indicates significant "Family Disease" and it is recommended that treatment should be sought through the appropriate Family Fellowship and possibly also through the family programme of a Minnesota Model treatment centre based upon the principles of the Anonymous Fellowships.

Recovery and Relapse Prevention

It is easy to mock and to say "Well, why don't I simply give up everything and become a hermit – or, better still, commit suicide". That is simply "disease talk": addictive disease speaking to the sufferer hrough his or her own mind. It needs to be recognised for the exaggerating, self-pitying garbage that it is.

From this PROMIS Handbook on Cross-Addiction it should be possible to identify those areas in which there is greatest risk of relapse. A general rule of thumb is that any area in which there are between one and nine positive answers indicates that there may well be addictive disease but that this particular area is probably not an area of great concern (although it may be helpful to see one's self more clearly by going through the questionnaire with someone who knows one well). An area with between ten and nineteen positive answers indicates a significant cross-addiction which will therefore be an area of risk for relapse. An area with twenty or more positive answers indicates a primary addiction.

In the first group of between one and nine positive answers there may be relatively little risk of cross-addiction. However, care should be taken not to take this reassurance to ridiculous extremes. For example, a low score on the questionnaires for alcohol or recreational drugs does not mean that someone can afford to get drunk or stoned without risk: addictive disease may soon enlarge any channel that the sufferer chooses to start digging.

It is advisable for any person suffering from *any* form of addictive disease to give up alcohol and recreational drugs and any prescription drugs that are mood altering. The risks of relapse are too great. The siren voices that call to "moderation" and "a balanced life" are treacherous voices where potentially addictive substances and behaviour are concerned.

In the second group of between ten and nineteen positive answers the sufferers will probably need to put down the specific substance or behaviour of addiction and will also be helped by going to some meet-ings of the appropriate Anonymous Fellowship. However, in this group the risk is that addictive disease may persuade the sufferer to focus much time and attention on relatively minor cross-addictions rather than upon the major primary addiction. The general principle of "first things first" should apply.

In the third category of twenty or more positive answers are the major primary addictions. Some people have more than one primary addic-tion. They would be best advised to give up the addictive substance or behaviour relevant to those particular addictions and to attend regular meetings of the appropriate Anonymous Fellowships.

Family Disease will require independent treatment through the Family Fellowships and possibly also through the family programmes of Minnesota Model treatment centres based upon the principles of the Anonymous Fellowships.

Some people just do have more addictive disease than others in the same way as some people have more short sight than others. If these people want to take recovery seriously then they will need to look seriously at each of these areas of potential cross-addiction and perhaps also at the possibility of Family Disease. This may seem a tall order but the alternative is worse.

The good news, if there is any, for people with major cross-addiction or multiple primary addictions, is that these people will have deeper than other's experience of addictive disease and hence also of recovery. In time they can be enormously encouraging and helpful to other peo-ple in early recovery from addictive disease and in this, following the basic principle first discovered by the co-founders of Alcoholics Anonymous, they will keep what they give away.